NSC
First Aid,
CPR & AED
WORKBOOK

187M0614

Interior design, layout and composition and cover design: Bending Design Inc.

Photo Credits: Cover: © iStockphoto/onebluelight; Page 26 (top right): iStockphoto/kbwills; Page 32 (top left): © Dr. P. Marazzi/Photo Researchers; Page 32 (top right): © Image courtesy Bradley R. Davis; Page 50 (top left): www.poison-ivy.org; Page 50 (top right): Courtesy M.D. Vaden, Certified Arborist, Oregon; Page 50 (bottom right): © Gilbert Grant/Photo Researchers; Page 54 (a): © Tom McHugh/Photo Researchers; Page 54 (b): © Jupiterimages/Thinkstock; Page 54 (c): Thinkstock; Page 54 (d): Suzanne L. Collins/Photo Researchers; Page 54 (e): © Tom Brakefield/Thinkstock; Page 54 (f) Thinkstock; Page 54 (g): Centers for Disease Control and Prevention; Page 54 (h): © Robert Noonan/Photo Researchers; Page 57 (top): © Mediscan; Page 57 (middle): © Mediscan; Page 59 (top): © Image courtesy Robb S. Rehberg; Page 59 (bottom): © Hans Neleman/Photonica/Getty. All other photographs © National Safety Council/Rick Brady, photographer.

DISCLAIMER

Although the information and recommendations contained in this publication have been compiled from sources believed to be reliable, the National Safety Council makes no guarantee as to, and assumes no responsibility for, the correctness, sufficiency, or completeness of such information or recommendations. Other or additional safety measures may be required under particular circumstances.

NATIONAL SAFETY COUNCIL MISSION STATEMENT

The National Safety Council saves lives by preventing injuries and deaths at work, in homes and communities, and on the roads through leadership, research, education and advocacy.

nsc.org

© 2011 National Safety Council
All Rights Reserved
Printed in the U.S.A.

ISBN: 978-0-87912-303-1

About The National Safety Council

The National Safety Council is a nonprofit organization whose mission is to save lives by preventing injuries and deaths at work, in homes and communities and on the road through leadership, research, education and advocacy. NSC advances this mission by partnering with businesses, government agencies, elected officials and the public to make an impact where the most preventable injuries and deaths occur, in areas such as distracted driving, teen driving, workplace safety and beyond the workplace, particularly in and near our homes.

Founded in 1913 and chartered by Congress, the National Safety Council relies on research to determine optimal solutions to safety issues. Its educational efforts aim to change behaviors by building awareness, providing training and sharing best practices. The Council recognizes organizations that have focused on safety as a critical part of their operational excellence with the Robert W. Campbell Award®, safety's most prestigious honor. NSC Congress & Expo is the world's largest annual event dedicated to safety and Safety+Health® magazine is a leading source of occupational safety information. Offering a variety of learning options, NSC is a leader in First Aid and Workplace Safety training and created the defensive driving course concept where it remains the chief innovator. Each year the Green Cross for Safety® medal from NSC salutes a company with an outstanding safety record for its leadership in responsible citizenship and community service. The World Health Organization named NSC as the designated U.S. certification center for Safe Communities America®.

The National Safety Council is committed to helping its members and the public prevent unintentional injuries and deaths by providing knowledge and resources that enable them to reduce risks, engage employees, measure progress and continuously improve their safety management systems. With local Chapters and global networks, NSC is the leading advocate for safety and promotes June as National Safety Month.

Author Acknowledgements

Many National Safety Council staff and affiliates have contributed to the production of this book, and we would like to acknowledge the following people for their assistance:

Paul Satterlee MD, for reviewing and providing oversight of content.

Goodman Research Inc., for program evaluation and recomendations for program improvement.

Tom Lochhaas, Editorial Services, for providing technical writing services.

Donna M. Siegfried, Senior Director, First Aid Programs, for providing vision and support.

Barbara Caracci, Director, Program Development and Training, for providing oversight of content, development and production.

Donna Fredenhagen, Product Manager, for providing marketing support.

Kathy Safranek, Project Administrator, for providing day-to-day assistance.

Roseann Solak, Manager, Product Development, for oversight management of development processes and design teams.

Pauline DePinto, Product Coordinator, for coordinating development and production.

Alice Spencer, Project Manager, for coordinating development and production.

The Council also recognizes with appreciation the many other NSC employees who devoted time to this project.

Reviewer Acknowledgements

Lucy Clarke, RN
Managing Director
Emergency Care Training (HK)
Hong Kong

Rebecca Gribben, BS, NREMT
Training Director
Advent Resource Management
Houston, TX

Linda Holmes, BS, RN
Finger Lakes DDSO
Rochester, NY

Patricia Jubinville, BS, EMT-P
Instructor Trainer
Safety Council of Central and
Western New York
East Syracuse, NY

Deb Kaye, BS NREMT
Director/Instructor EMS
Dakota County Technical College
Rosemount, MN

David Morgan, EMT, BS
Principal Trainer
Safety First
Newark, NJ

Wade Skinner
Advisor – Safety and Health
Kennecott Utah Copper
South Jordan, UT

Kevin Stewart, EMT-B
First Aid and Membership
    Services Coordinator
North Dakota Safety Council
Bismark, ND

Jack Weberg
Instructor/Instructor Trainer
Arizona Chapter, National Safety
Council
Phoenix, AZ

Table of Contents

Lesson 1 • Acting in an Emergency

Objectives

✓ State how your actions can make a difference to a victim of injury or sudden illness.

✓ List the goals of first aid and basic life support.

✓ Identify how to contact Emergency Medical Services (EMS).

✓ List ways to be prepared in case of an emergency.

✓ Describe when consent is needed for helping a victim.

✓ List 6 steps to take in all emergencies.

✓ Describe when to call 9-1-1 and what information to give.

Video Review

1. What are your 4 goals when you help a victim?

_____

_____

_____

_____

Circle T for true or F for false for each of the following statements.

2. T   F   Check the victim quickly before calling 9-1-1.

3. T   F   Ask a responsive adult for consent for you to give care.

4. T   F   Do not move a victim unnecessarily.

5. You should follow the same 6 steps in any emergency. Write in the missing steps:

1. Recognize the emergency.

2. _Ensure scene is safe_

3. _Ask consent if possible_

4. Call 9-1-1 (when appropriate).

5. Care for the person.

6. Have the person seek medical attention when needed.

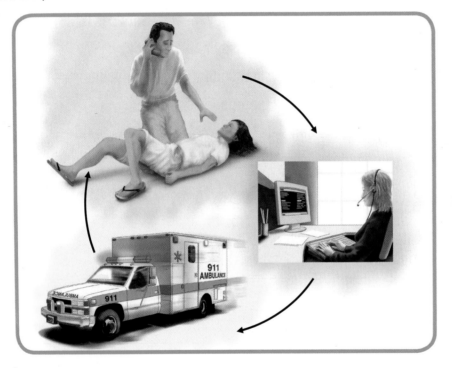

CALLING 9-1-1

When calling 9-1-1, be prepared to give this information to the dispatcher:

- Your name
- The phone number you are using
- The location and number of victims
- The victim's approximate age, sex and condition (responsive? breathing? bleeding?)
- What happened to the victim and any special circumstances
- What is being done for the victim

The dispatcher may also give you instructions on how to help the victim. Stay on the line until the dispatcher says you can hang up.

Things to Remember

ACTING IN AN EMERGENCY

- Your primary goal is to ensure the victim gets help quickly.
- Call 9-1-1 or your local emergency number for all emergencies.
- Give victims only the care you have been trained in.
- Always check the scene for safety and then the victim before beginning to provide care.

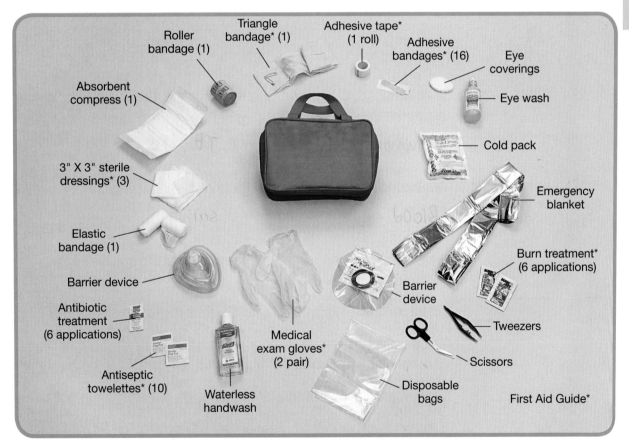

Roller bandage (1)
Triangle bandage* (1)
Adhesive tape* (1 roll)
Adhesive bandages* (16)
Eye coverings
Absorbent compress (1)
Eye wash
Cold pack
3" X 3" sterile dressings* (3)
Emergency blanket
Elastic bandage (1)
Burn treatment* (6 applications)
Barrier device
Barrier device
Antibiotic treatment (6 applications)
Tweezers
Medical exam gloves* (2 pair)
Scissors
Antiseptic towelettes* (10)
Disposable bags
Waterless handwash
First Aid Guide*

Components of a first aid kit. Include optional supplies based on specific hazards in a particular work environment.

*Minimum requirements for workplace first aid kit.

Lesson 2 • Preventing Disease Transmission

Objectives

✓ List standard precautions to prevent transmission of disease.

✓ Identify personal protective equipment (PPE) to protect yourself from infection.

✓ Demonstrate how to take off medical exam gloves.

Video Review

1. What kinds of diseases could be spread during first aid *if you do not take precautions?*

   COMMON COLD   TB, Hep,

2. Give examples of body fluids you should avoid contact with.

   Blood   Saliva

3. What precautions can you take to prevent exposure to a victim's body fluids? (Check all that apply.)

   ☐ Use personal protective equipment such as medical exam gloves.

   ☐ If you do not have medical exam gloves, put your hands in plastic bags or have the victim dress the wound.

   ☐ Wash your hands with soap and water before and after giving first aid.

   ☐ Do not touch your mouth, nose or eyes when giving first aid (do not eat, drink or smoke).

   ☐ Use an alcohol-based hand gel if soap and water are not available.

   ☐ If you are exposed to blood or a body fluid, wash immediately with soap and water then call your health care provider. At work, report the situation to your supervisor.

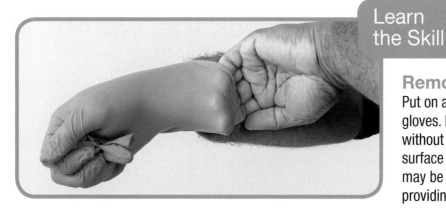

Removing Gloves

Put on a pair of medical exam gloves. Practice removing them without touching the outer surface of the gloves, which may be contaminated after providing first aid.

Performance Checklist: Glove Removal

Skill Step		Needs Practice	Proficient
1	Hold your hands away from your body, with fingers pointing down.		
2	With 1 hand, grasp your other glove at the wrist or palm and pull it away from your hand. Then pull the glove the rest of the way off.		
3	Holding the removed glove balled up in the palm of your gloved hand, insert 2 fingers under the cuff of the remaining glove.		
4	Remove the glove by stretching it up and away from the hand and turning it inside out as you pull it off.		
5	Dispose of gloves safely and wash your hands.		
	Complete Skill		

Things to Remember

PREVENTING DISEASE TRANSMISSION

- Avoid contact with all body fluids.
- Use gloves and other barrier devices.
- Follow precautions to prevent exposure to pathogens, which cause disease.
- Decontaminate all surfaces as soon as possible with a commercial body fluid disposal kit. Or, clean with detergent, rinse with water, then sanitize with a 10% bleach/water solution. Leave bleach solution on the spill for at least 2 minutes before wiping it.

View the OSHA Standard, Bloodborne Pathogens (1910.1030) at http://www.osha.gov/pls/oshaweb/owadisp.show_document?p_table=STANDARDS&p_id=10051.

Lesson 3 • Check the Victim

Objectives

✓ Describe how to perform the initial assessment of a victim.
✓ List the parts of the victim's history to obtain.
✓ Describe how to perform a physical examination.
✓ Demonstrate how to check the victim for life-threatening problems.

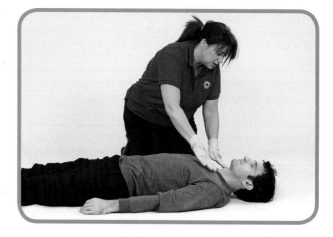

 Video Review

Circle T for true or F for false for each of the following statements.

1. **T** F After determining the scene is safe, the first thing you should do when you approach a victim is check for responsiveness and normal breathing.

2. T **F** If the victim occasionally seems to gasp, this means the victim is breathing normally.

3. T **F** Do not stop to call 9-1-1 until you've checked the victim all over and have bandaged any bleeding wounds.

4. **T** F Check a breathing victim immediately for bleeding that may be life-threatening.

5. T **F** If you find a person who is not breathing normally, conduct a full physical examination to look for possible causes.

Learn the Skill

Initial Assessment
Pair up with another classmate to practice the initial assessment of an unresponsive victim.

Performance Checklist: Initial Assessment

Skill Step		Needs Practice	Proficient
1	Check for responsiveness and normal breathing.		
2	If the victim is unresponsive, call 9-1-1. If the victim is unresponsive and not breathing, also call for an AED and provide basic life support.		
3	If the victim is breathing, check for severe bleeding and other threats to life.		
4	Care for any life-threatening conditions before continuing to check the victim and provide other care.		
Complete Skill			

The Victim's History

Talk to a responsive victim or ask bystanders to find out more about what happened and the victim's condition. The SAMPLE history format is a tool that may help you remember the kinds of questions to ask:

S = Signs and symptoms
A = Allergies
M = Medications
P = Previous problems
L = Last food or drink
E = Events

A victim may be awake but confused. Ask the victim his name, where he is and for the time, day or date. A victim's answers reflect his mental status.

Give information about the victim's mental status and history to arriving EMS personnel.

3 • Check the Victim

Physical Examination of an Injured Victim

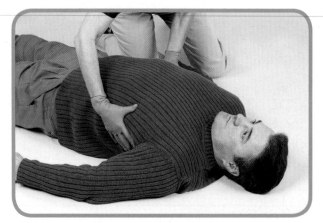

Unless you are giving first aid for a serious condition, examine an injured victim from head to toe, looking for anything out of the ordinary:

- Pain when an area is touched

- Bleeding or other wounds

- An area that is swollen or deformed

- Skin color (flushed or pale), temperature (hot or cold), condition (dry, sweating or clammy)

- Abnormal sensation or movement of the area

- A medical alert ID

Give first aid for any problems you find.

Things to Remember

CHECKING A VICTIM

- Always check first for responsiveness and normal breathing.
- Call 9-1-1 for any unresponsive victim. Call also for an AED for any unresponsive victim not breathing normally.
- Check for severe bleeding.
- Care for any life-threatening problems.
- Get the victim's history and do a physical exam only if there are no serious problems that need care.

Lesson 4 • Basic Life Support

Objectives

- ✓ Identify when basic life support (BLS) is needed.
- ✓ Identify the links in the cardiac chain of survival.
- ✓ State when cardiopulmonary resuscitation (CPR) is needed.
- ✓ Identify the correct hand position for chest compressions.
- ✓ Identify the correct rate and depth of chest compressions.
- ✓ Identify when and how rescue breaths are given.
- ✓ Identify how to correctly perform the head tilt–chin lift.
- ✓ Identify the importance of using a barrier device for rescue breaths.
- ✓ Identify the correct ratio of chest compressions to breaths.
- ✓ Identify when CPR can stop.
- ✓ Identify when and how Hands-Only CPR is given.
- ✓ Identify when and how to use an automated external defibrillator (AED).
- ✓ Demonstrate how to give CPR to an adult, child and infant.
- ✓ Demonstrate how to use an AED on an adult, child and infant.

The Cardiac Chain of Survival

If someone's heart stops, quick action is needed!

1. **Immediate recognition of the cardiac arrest and activation of the emergency response system** – identify the emergency and call for help (9-1-1 or local emergency number).

2. **Early CPR with emphasis on chest compressions** – call for an AED and start CPR immediately.

3. **Rapid defibrillation** – use the AED as soon as it is available.

4. **Effective advanced life support** – the sooner the victim receives professional care, the better the chance for survival.

5. **Integrated post-cardiac arrest care** – the victim needs continued medical care.

Performance Checklist: CPR

Skill Step		Needs Practice	Proficient
1	For an unresponsive victim who is not breathing or only gasps occasionally, send someone to call 9-1-1 (or your local emergency number) and get an AED. If alone with an adult, first call 9-1-1 and get an AED if available nearby. If alone with a child, first give 2 minutes of CPR and then call 9-1-1 and get an AED if available.		
2	Expose the chest. Place hands in correct position for chest compressions. • *For adults: in center of chest, with 1 hand on top of the other.* • *For children: in center of chest with 1 or 2 hands.* • *For infants: 2 middle fingers of 1 hand just below the nipple line.* • *Do not give compressions over the bottom tip of the breastbone.* • *For an adult or child, keep fingers off the chest and do not lean on the chest.* • *Keep your elbows straight and keep your hands in contact with the chest at all times.*		
3	Give 30 chest compressions at a rate of at least 100 per minute. Count aloud for a steady fast rate: "1, 2, 3 . . . ." • *For adults: to a depth of at least 2 inches.* • *For children (age 1 to puberty): to a depth of 1/3 the depth of the chest or about 2 inches.* • *For infants (to age 1): to a depth of 1/3 the depth of the chest, or about 1½ inches.* • *Let the chest rise completely after each compression.*		
4	Tilt the head and lift the chin to open the airway. Give 2 rescue breaths, each lasting 1 second. (If the first breath does not go in, reposition the head and try again; if the second breath does not go in, look in the mouth and remove any object seen.)		
5	Continue cycles of 30 compressions and 2 breaths.		
6	Continue CPR until: • Victim wakes up. • An AED is brought to the scene and is ready to use. • Professional help arrives and takes over.		
7	a. If the victim is breathing normally but is unresponsive, put the victim in the recovery position and monitor breathing. b. When an AED arrives, start the AED sequence.		
	Complete Skill		

Performance Checklist: AED

Skill Step		Needs Practice	Proficient
1	Position victim away from water and metal. Place unit by victim's shoulder and turn it on.		
2	Expose victim's chest and quickly dry or shave the pad placement areas if necessary.		
3	Apply pads to victim's chest as shown on pads. If needed, plug cables into unit. *Use adult pads for a victim age 8 or older. For an infant or child under age 8, use a unit with pediatric pads if available, applied as directed by the unit; if pediatric pads are unavailable, use adult pads.*		
4	Stand clear during rhythm analysis.		
5	Follow prompts from AED unit to take 1 of 3 actions: (1) press the shock button, (2) stay clear while the AED automatically delivers a shock or (3) do not shock but immediately give CPR with the pads remaining in place, starting with chest compressions.		
6	Follow the AED's prompts to analyze the rhythm again after 5 cycles of CPR (about 2 minutes).		
7	Continue steps 5 and 6 until the victim wakes up or professional rescuers arrive and take over.		
8	If the victim is breathing normally but is unresponsive, put the victim in the recovery position (with pads remaining in place) and continue to monitor the breathing.		
	Complete Skill		

Scenarios for Additional Practice
Scenario 1: The Jogger

You are at the beach with a group of people when a man jogging by suddenly collapses and falls face down on the sand. Provide basic life support from the moment you arrive at the victim's side, with all actions in the correct sequence. Follow your instructor's descriptions of how the victim responds.

Scenario 2: The Baseball Game

You are at a youth baseball game when a child at bat is struck in the chest by a pitch. He falls to the ground and does not move. Provide basic life support with all actions in the correct sequence. Follow your instructor's descriptions of how the victim responds.

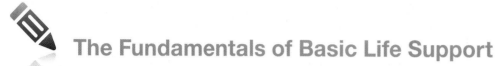

The Fundamentals of Basic Life Support

Fill in the correct answers:

1. For an adult you see collapse, start CPR as soon as you determine the victim is

   _____ and not _____ normally.

2. In each cycle of CPR, rapidly compress the chest _____ times and then give _____ breaths.

3. If the AED advises giving a shock, immediately after this shock you should perform CPR starting with

   _____ _____ for about _____ minutes and then follow the AED prompts.

Circle T for true or F for false for each of the following statements:

4. If you are alone with an adult you see collapse suddenly, you should call 9-1-1 before starting to give CPR.

   T F

5. Give chest compressions at a rate of 1 every second.

   T F

6. It is okay to use pediatric AED pads on an adult.

   T F

7. When giving a breath during CPR, breathe into the victim for about 1 second.

   T F

8. When giving chest compressions, allow the chest to move all the way back up between compressions.

   T F

9. Begin CPR with 2 quick breaths before starting compressions.

   T F

Things to Remember

KEY PRINCIPLES OF BASIC LIFE SUPPORT

- Call 9-1-1 or your local emergency number for an unresponsive victim.
- For unresponsive victims who are not breathing normally, use the CPR technique that allows you to confidently deliver good-quality chest compressions with minimal interruption – either conventional CPR or Hands-Only CPR.
- For conventional CPR:
  - Begin with 30 chest compressions hard and fast in the center of the chest. Compress the chest at least 2 inches for an adult or at least ⅓ the depth of the chest in an infant (about 1½ inches) or child (about 2 inches), giving compressions at a rate of at least 100 per minute.
  - Open the airway with the head tilt–chin lift and give 2 breaths, each for about 1 second, watching the chest rise and fall. Use a barrier device to give breaths, if available.
  - Continue with cycles of 30 compressions and 2 breaths.
- For Hands-Only CPR:
  - Push hard and fast in the center of the chest.
- Use the AED as soon as it is available and ready to use.
  - Apply the pads to the victim's chest as shown on the pads. For an infant or child under age 8, use a unit with pediatric pads if available.
  - Follow the AED prompts to give a shock when indicated and then to continue CPR before the AED again analyzes the victim's rhythm.
  - If the victim begins breathing normally but remains unresponsive, position the victim in the recovery position and monitor breathing until help arrives.

Lesson 5 • Recovery Position

Objectives

✓ Identify the purpose of the recovery position.

✓ Demonstrate how to put an unresponsive breathing adult in the recovery position.

Video Review

1. Use the HAINES (**H**igh **A**rm **IN E**ndangered **S**pine) recovery position for any victim who is _____ and _____.

2. What are the benefits of the recovery position? (Check all that apply.)

   ❑ It helps the heart beat more efficiently.

   ❑ It allows the person to breathe more easily.

   ❑ It allows fluids to drain from the mouth.

   ❑ It helps the body stay warm.

   ❑ It prevents inhalation of stomach contents if the victim vomits.

   ❑ It helps control bleeding of the extremities.

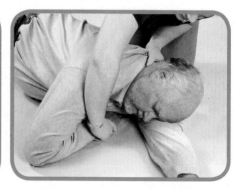

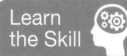

Putting a Victim in the Recovery Position
Pair up with another person in the class to practice putting an unresponsive victim in the recovery position.

Performance Checklist: HAINES Recovery Position

Skill Step		Needs Practice	Proficient
1	Extend the victim's arm that is farther from you above the victim's head.		
2	Position the victim's other arm across the chest.		
3	Bend the victim's nearer leg at the knee.		
4	Put your forearm under the victim's shoulder with your hand around the back of the neck to support the head and neck.		
5	Carefully roll the victim away from you by pushing on the victim's flexed knee and lifting with your forearm while your hand stabilizes the head and neck. The victim's head is now supported on the raised arm.		
6	While continuing to support the head and neck, position the victim's hand palm-down with fingers under the armpit of the raised arm, with forearm flat on the surface at 90 degrees to the body.		
7	Bend both legs so the victim's position is stabilized.		
8	With victim now in position, open the mouth to allow drainage and monitor breathing.		
Complete Skill			

5 • Recovery Position

Things to Remember

RECOVERY POSITION

- Use the recovery position for any unresponsive victim who is breathing.

Lesson 6 • Choking

Objectives

✓ Identify correct choking care for a responsive adult, child or infant with a partially obstructed airway who can cough.

✓ Identify how to give abdominal thrusts to a responsive choking adult or child.

✓ Identify correct care for a choking victim who becomes unresponsive.

✓ Demonstrate how to provide choking care for a responsive adult or child.

✓ Demonstrate how to provide choking care for a responsive infant.

Video Review

1. If you believe a person is choking, what should you ask that person?

   _____

2. Where do you position your hands to give abdominal thrusts to a responsive choking victim?

   _____

3. In what direction do you provide the abdominal thrusts?

   _____

4. What is different about CPR given to an unresponsive choking victim, compared with conventional CPR for a victim not known to be choking?

   _____

Choking Care for Responsive Adult or Child

Pair up with a classmate to practice choking care for a responsive victim. *Do not actually give abdominal thrusts to the other participant – this skill is to learn hand and body position.*

Performance Checklist: Choking Care for Responsive Adult or Child

Skill Step		Needs Practice	Proficient
1	Stand behind the victim with 1 leg forward between the victim's legs. For a child, move down to the child's level. Keep your head slightly to 1 side.		
2	Locate the person's navel with a finger from 1 hand.		
3	Make a fist with the other hand and place the thumb side of the fist against the person's abdomen just above the navel.		
4	Grasp your fist with your other hand and thrust inward and upward into the victim's abdomen with quick jerks. Continue abdominal thrusts until the victim expels the object or becomes unresponsive.		
5	For a responsive pregnant victim or any victim you cannot get your arms around or for whom abdominal thrusts are not effective, give chest thrusts from behind the victim. Avoid squeezing the ribs with your arms.		
6	If the victim becomes unresponsive (or for any choking victim found unresponsive), lower the person to the ground, expose the chest and start CPR with 30 chest compressions. Look inside the mouth each time you open the mouth to give breaths and remove any object seen.		
Complete Skill			

6 • Choking

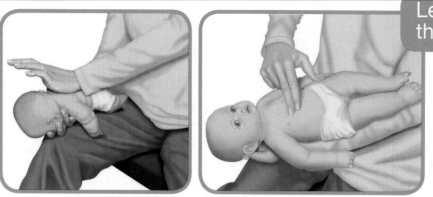

Learn the Skill

Choking Care for Responsive Infant

Practice with an infant manikin.
Remember: Give choking care only if the infant cannot cry, cough or breathe.

Performance Checklist: Choking Care for Responsive Infant

	Skill Step	Needs Practice	Proficient
1	Support the infant face down by holding the head in 1 hand, with the torso on your forearm against your thigh. Give up to 5 back blows (slaps) between the shoulder blades with the heel of your other hand.		
2	If the object is not expelled, roll the infant face up, supporting the back of the infant's head with your hand.		
3	Place 2 fingers on the breastbone, just below the nipple line.		
4	Give 5 chest thrusts, about 1 per second. Each thrust should be 1½ inches deep.		
5	Continue cycles of 5 back blows (slaps) and 5 chest thrusts until the object is expelled or the infant becomes unresponsive. If alone, call 9-1-1 after 1 minute.		
6	If the infant becomes unresponsive (or for any choking infant found unresponsive), give CPR. Look inside the mouth each time you open the mouth to give breaths and remove any object seen.		
	Complete Skill		

FIRST AID FOR CHOKING

- If the person is coughing productively, encourage continued coughing to expel the obstructing item on his or her own.
- If the person clutches his or her throat, looks frantic or signals he or she is not getting enough air:
  1. Ask if the person is choking. If the victim nods or indicates yes, ask if you can help.
  2. Take position behind the victim, with your leg between his or her legs and your fist just above the navel.
  3. Give quick thrusts inward and upward to clear the object.
- If a choking victim becomes unresponsive, give CPR starting with chest compressions. Look inside the mouth each time you open the mouth to give breaths and remove any object seen.

Lesson 7 • Heart Attack and Chest Pain

Objectives

✓ Describe the signs and symptoms of heart attack.

✓ List the general steps of first aid for heart attack.

✓ Differentiate between heart attack and angina.

Video Review

Heart Attack

1. List as many of the possible heart attack signs and symptoms as you can:

_____

_____

_____

_____

_____

2. When should you call 9-1-1 for a possible heart attack?

_____

3. What first aid can you provide for a possible heart attack?

_____

_____

_____

Scenario 1: Aunt Ursula

First read the scenario, then talk with another participant sitting beside you about what you would do.

Aunt Ursula is visiting your family for a few days. She generally seems to be in good health. About an hour after a big holiday meal, she says she doesn't feel well. She has been feeling pressure in her chest since she ate and she is sweating. Remembering your first aid course, you think she might be having a heart attack, but she says she thinks it's only indigestion caused by all that food. "I don't want to cause trouble for anyone," she says. "I'll just sit here until it goes away."

What do you say to her? If she keeps insisting that it's only indigestion, what can you do?

Angina

The chest pain of angina usually happens after intense activity or exertion, is recognized as angina by the victim and lasts only a few minutes.

- Ask if the person has been diagnosed with angina and if the pain is like angina pain experienced in the past. If so, help the person take his or her own medication and rest.

- Call 9-1-1 and give heart attack first aid if –
    - The pain lasts longer than 10 minutes
    - The pain goes away but then comes back
    - The person has other heart attack symptoms not relieved by rest

7 • Heart Attack and Chest Pain

Things to Remember

FIRST AID FOR HEART ATTACK

1. Call 9-1-1 for any person experiencing chest discomfort, even if the victim says it is not serious.
2. Help the victim rest in a comfortable position. Loosen constricting clothing.
3. Ask the victim if he or she is taking heart medication and help obtain the medication. Follow the directions on the medication.
4. Encourage the victim to chew 1 uncoated adult or 2 low-dose baby aspirin unless he or she is allergic to aspirin or cannot take aspirin for any other reason.
5. Stay with the victim and be reassuring and calming.
6. Be ready to give basic life support if needed.
7. Do not let the victim eat or drink anything (including water).

Lesson 8 • Bleeding and Wound Care

Objectives

✓ Identify how to control bleeding with direct pressure.

✓ Demonstrate how to control bleeding.

✓ Demonstrate how to apply a pressure bandage.

✓ Describe how to clean and dress a minor wound.

✓ List signs and symptoms of wound infection.

✓ Identify when to seek medical attention for a wound.

✓ Determine when a tetanus booster is needed.

✓ Identify the care needed for:

- Puncture wounds
- Impaled objects
- Amputations
- Genital injuries
- Head and face injuries
- Eye injuries
- Ear injuries
- Nose injuries
- Mouth injuries
- Animal or human bites

✓ Describe the care for internal bleeding.

Video Review

Circle T for true or F for false for each of the following statements.

1. (T) F The most effective way to stop bleeding is to put firm pressure directly on a dressing over the wound with a gloved hand.

2. T (F) To clean a small wound once bleeding has stopped, pour rubbing alcohol on it.

3. (T) F A victim with a gaping wound or a deep puncture wound should seek medical attention.

Scenario 1: The Lunch Room

A co-worker has cut her forearm badly with a knife in the lunch room. Another employee calls 9-1-1 and runs for the first aid kit while you help the victim. You do not have gloves with you. What can you do to control the bleeding?

Bleeding Control

Pair up with a classmate to practice controlling bleeding in an extremity.

Performance Checklist: Bleeding Control

Skill Step		Needs Practice	Proficient
1	Put on gloves. *Improvise a barrier if no gloves are available.*		
2	Place a sterile dressing or clean cloth on the wound.		
3	Apply firm, direct pressure with your hand for about 5 minutes. *Do not put pressure on an object in a wound.* *Do not put pressure on the scalp if the skull may be injured.*		
4	Reevaluate the bleeding: If it continues, put another dressing or cloth pad on top of the first and keep applying pressure.		
5	If needed, apply a pressure bandage to keep pressure on the wound, wrapping from the end of the extremity toward the center of the body. *The pressure is sufficient if the bandage is snug but you can slip a finger under it.* *Tourniquets only should be used as an extreme last resort by rescuers trained in their use because of the high risk of complications.*		
6	If appropriate, treat the victim for shock and call 9-1-1.		
	Complete Skill		

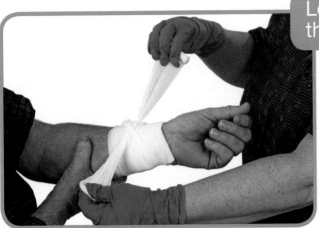

Learn the Skill

Applying a Pressure Bandage

Pair up with a classmate to practice applying a pressure bandage to an extremity.

Performance Checklist: Pressure Bandage

Skill Step		Needs Practice	Proficient
1	Anchor the starting end of the elastic or self-adhering bandage below the wound dressing.		
2	Make several circular turns.		
3	Work up the limb in overlapping turns.		
4	Fix or tie the end of the bandage in place. *The pressure is sufficient if the bandage is snug but a finger can be slipped under it.*		
	Complete Skill		

Wound Care

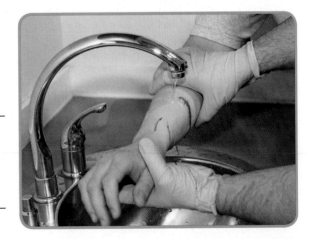

1. How should you clean a wound with dirt in it?

_____

2. When should you put an antibiotic ointment on a wound?

_____

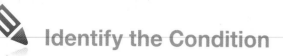

Identify the Condition

1. What is likely wrong with this wounded finger?

_____

2. If your finger looked like this 4 days after being injured, what should you do?

_____

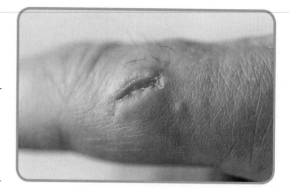

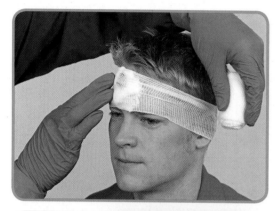

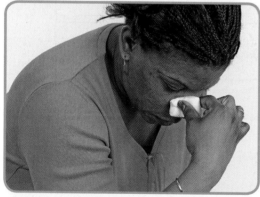

Care of Special Wounds

Consult your *First Aid Quick Guide* 📖 for the first aid steps for these special kinds of wounds:

- Puncture wounds
- Impaled objects
- Amputations
- Genital injuries
- Head and face injuries
- Eye injuries
- Ear injuries
- Nose bleeding or injury
- Mouth injuries
- Animal or human bites
- Crush injuries

Internal Bleeding

Use your *First Aid Quick Guide* to answer the following questions.

1. Write down at least 3 signs and symptoms of internal bleeding:

_____

_____

_____

2. What is the single most important action to take for a victim with internal bleeding?

_____

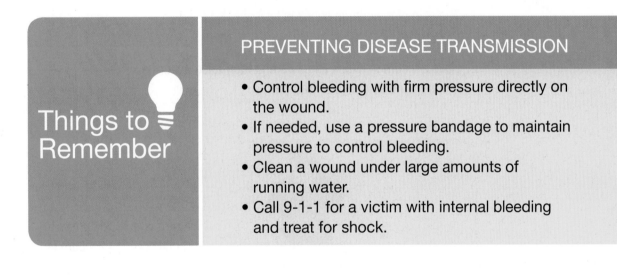

Things to Remember

PREVENTING DISEASE TRANSMISSION

- Control bleeding with firm pressure directly on the wound.
- If needed, use a pressure bandage to maintain pressure to control bleeding.
- Clean a wound under large amounts of running water.
- Call 9-1-1 for a victim with internal bleeding and treat for shock.

Lesson 9 • Shock

Objectives

✓ List the causes of shock.

✓ Identify the signs and symptoms of shock.

✓ Identify the first aid for shock.

✓ Demonstrate how to put a victim in the shock position.

Video Review

1. The skin of a victim in shock is typically <u>cool</u> and <u>clammy</u>.

2. Have a victim in shock lie down and then raise his or her <u>legs</u> if there is no evidence of trauma.

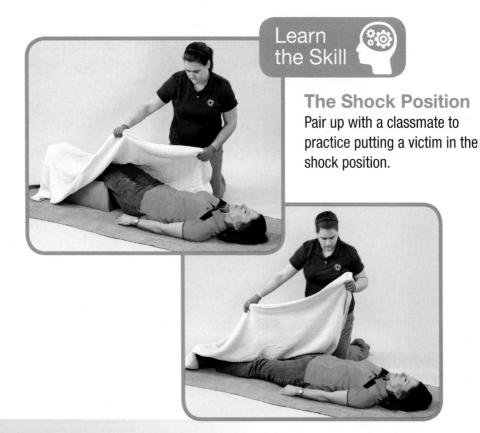

Learn the Skill

The Shock Position
Pair up with a classmate to practice putting a victim in the shock position.

Performance Checklist: Shock Position

Skill Step		Needs Practice	Proficient
1	Check for responsiveness, normal breathing and severe bleeding or injuries.		
2	Call 9-1-1 and be ready to give basic life support if needed.		
3	Care first for life-threatening conditions such as severe bleeding.		
4	a. Position a responsive victim on his or her back using a blanket or coat as a pad. If there is no evidence of trauma, raise the legs such that the feet are 6-12 inches above the ground. b. Put a breathing, unresponsive victim (if no suspected spinal injury) in the recovery position.		
5	Loosen any tight clothing.		
6	Be alert for the possibility of vomiting; turn the victim's head to drain the mouth.		
7	Maintain the victim's normal body temperature. If necessary, maintain the victim's body heat with a blanket or coat over the victim.		
8	Do not let a shock victim eat, drink or smoke.		
9	Stay with the victim and offer reassurance and comfort.		
Complete Skill			

9 • Shock

Things to Remember

FIRST AID FOR SHOCK

Signs and symptoms
- Anxiety, confusion, agitation or restlessness
- Dizziness, lightheadedness
- Cool, clammy or sweating skin that is pale, bluish or ashen in color
- Rapid, shallow breathing
- Thirst
- Nausea, vomiting
- Changing levels of responsiveness

First Aid
1. Check for responsiveness, normal breathing and severe bleeding or injuries.
2. Call 9-1-1 and care first for life-threatening conditions such as severe bleeding.
3. Be ready to give basic life support if needed.
4. If there is no evidence of trauma, position a responsive victim on his or her back using a blanket or coat as a pad. Unless there is evidence of trauma, raise the legs such that the feet are 6-12 inches above the ground. Put a breathing unresponsive victim (if no suspected spinal injury) in the recovery position.
5. Loosen any tight clothing.
6. Be alert for the possibility of vomiting; turn the victim's head to drain the mouth.
7. Try to maintain the victim's normal body temperature. If necessary, maintain the victim's body heat with a blanket or coat over the victim.
8. Do not let a shock victim eat, drink or smoke.
9. Stay with victim and offer reassurance and comfort.

Lesson 10 • Burns

Objectives

✓ Differentiate among first-, second- and third-degree burns.

✓ Determine first aid for first-degree heat burns.

✓ Identify first aid for second- and third-degree heat burns.

✓ Identify first aid for chemical burns.

✓ Identify first aid for electrical burns and shocks.

Video Review

1. What are the first things you do for a serious burn?

   _____

2. Why would you not put water on a burn that covers more than 20% of the body?

   _____

3. How long should you flush the skin with water for a chemical burn?

   _____

Differences Between Second- and Third-Degree Burns

Second-degree burns

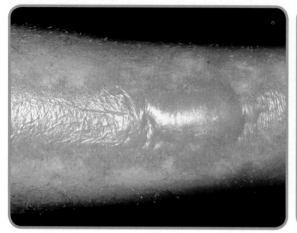

Third-degree burns

- Skin is swollen and red, may be blotchy or streaked

- Blisters that may be weeping clear fluid, moist-appearing skin

- Signs of significant pain

- Skin damage, charred skin or white leathery or waxy appearance

- May have signs and symptoms of shock

- May not be as painful

Scenario 1: A Burned Arm

Your friend has just burned his arm – it looks like a small second-degree burn. You grab a nearby hose and cool the burned area with cold running water. Then you get your first aid kit, where you keep your *First Aid Quick Guide* 📖.

Look up what to do now for the burn.

_____

_____

_____

_____

_____

Scenario 2: Chemical Spill

You enter an outdoor storage area where you work and find a co-worker frantically trying to rub a white powder from his arm. Beside him on the ground is a broken container that is leaking a chemical. How can you help?

_____

_____

_____

_____

Poisonous Fumes and Chemicals

1. Write in step numbers to put these actions in correct order for a victim who has inhaled poisonous fumes from a fire. (Check your *First Aid Quick Guide* .)

   ____ Help the victim into position for easiest breathing.

   ____ Get the victim to fresh air.

   ____ Call 9-1-1.

2. In your home or at work, do you work with any chemicals or liquids likely to cause a burn if splashed on you?

   _____

   _____

3. If so, what would you do if this substance splashed in your eyes?

   _____

   _____

Things to Remember

FIRST AID FOR FIRST- AND SECOND-DEGREE BURNS

1. Stop the burning by removing the heat source.
2. Immediately cool the burn with cold running tap water until area is free from pain even after removal from water. (Do not put ice on a burn.)
3. Remove constricting clothing and jewelry.
4. For large second-degree burns, call 9-1-1.
5. Protect the burn area with a loose, nonstick dressing.
6. Keep burn blisters intact.
7. Seek medical attention for burns on the face, genitals, hands or feet.

Additional First Aid for Third-Degree Burns:
- Do not cool a burn that covers more than 20% of the body with water (10% for child) because of the risk of hypothermia and shock.
- Call 9-1-1.
- Treat shock: have victim lie on back, elevate legs if no trauma and maintain normal body temperature.
- Do not give the victim anything to drink.
- Watch the victim's breathing and be ready to give basic life support if needed.

Lesson 11 • Serious Injuries

Objectives

✓ Identify situations when a spinal injury is possible.

✓ Identify first aid for a spinal injury.

✓ Demonstrate spinal motion restriction for spinal injuries.

✓ Identify first aid for:

- Broken ribs
- Objects impaled in the chest
- Sucking chest wounds
- Open abdominal injuries
- Closed abdominal injuries
- Hip injuries

Video Review

1. List some risk factors that should make you suspect a spinal injury.

_____   _____

_____   _____

_____   _____

2. Which of the following are actions you should take for a victim with a suspected spinal injury? (Check all that apply.)

❑ Do not touch the victim anywhere.

❑ Have someone call 9-1-1.

❑ Put the victim's head on a pillow to be in line with the spine.

❑ Stabilize the victim's head and neck in the position found.

❑ Place ice bags all over and around the neck.

❑ Drive the victim to a hospital emergency department as soon as possible.

Learn the Skill

Spinal Motion Restriction

Pair up with a classmate to practice spinal motion restriction.

Performance Checklist: Spinal Motion Restriction

Skill Step		Needs Practice	Proficient
1	Ask a responsive victim what happened. If he or she has any of the risk factors, explain the need to hold the head still to prevent spinal movement and spinal cord injury. With an unresponsive victim, check for risk factors for suspected spinal injury.		
2	Hold the victim's head and neck with both hands in the position found to prevent movement		
3	Monitor the victim's breathing and be ready to provide basic life support.		
4	Have someone call 9-1-1.		
5	Reassure a conscious victim and tell him or her not to move.		
6	Continue to stabilize head/spine and monitor the victim's breathing until help arrives.		
Complete Skill			

Scenario 1: Co-Worker Struck in the Head

A co-worker was struck in the head by a piece of machinery and is lying on the floor when you find him. He is breathing and his scalp is bleeding above 1 ear. You put on gloves and gently touch the bleeding area with a piece of gauze. You feel a small depressed area in the skull bone.

1. What must you not do when you try to control the bleeding?

_____

2. How should you try to control the bleeding?

_____

3. Can you move this victim to look for other injuries to his body? Why or why not?

_____

Chest Injuries

Refer to your *First Aid Quick Guide* for the first aid for these chest injuries.

Broken ribs

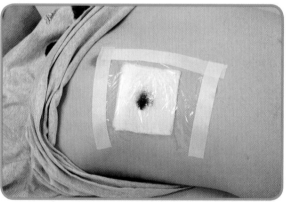

Sucking chest wound

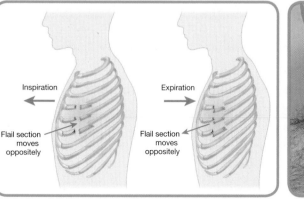

Flail chest

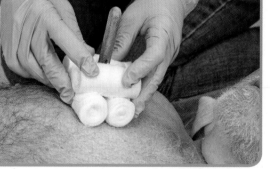

Impaled object

Open and Closed Abdominal Injuries

What is the single most important action to take for a victim with an abdominal injury?

_____

Consult your *First Aid Quick Guide* 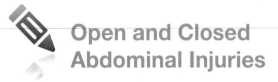 if you are unsure of the answer.

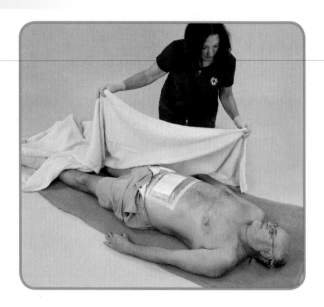

Hip Injuries

Use your *First Aid Quick Guide* to look up "Hip Injuries" and answer the following questions:

1. An elderly woman slips and falls. She says she has terrible pain in 1 hip. She is pale, her skin is cool and clammy, and she is becoming confused. What should you do immediately?

_____

2. In addition to the hip injury, what life-threatening condition is this woman probably experiencing?

   a. Cardiac arrest   b. Stroke   c. Shock   d. Anaphylaxis

3. What else can you do for her while waiting for help to arrive?

_____

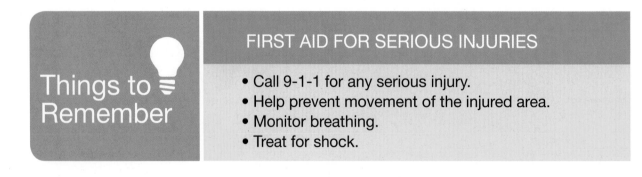

Things to Remember

FIRST AID FOR SERIOUS INJURIES

- Call 9-1-1 for any serious injury.
- Help prevent movement of the injured area.
- Monitor breathing.
- Treat for shock.

Lesson 12 • Bone, Joint and Muscle Injuries

Objectives

✓ Identify first aid for:

- Fractures
- Strains
- Dislocations
- Bruises
- Sprains
- Cramps

✓ Identify how to use rest, ice, compression and elevation (RICE) for an injury.

✓ Describe different types of splints.

✓ Identify guidelines for safe splinting.

Video Review

1. The signs and symptoms of a bone or joint injury include which of the following? (Check all that apply.)

   ❑ Deformed area   ❑ Small or unequal pupils

   ❑ Skin is hot and red   ❑ Swelling

   ❑ Pain   ❑ Inability to use body part

   ❑ Fever

2. Write out the meaning of RICE:

   R = _____

   I = _____

   C = _____

   E = _____

3. Do you ever need to call 9-1-1 for an injury of a bone, joint or muscle?

   _____

Scenario 1: An Incident at Work

At the loading dock at work, you see a worker who is struck by a large piece of equipment that falls off a forklift. The worker is lying on the ground in obvious pain when you approach. His forearm seems bent, and when you carefully cut through the bloody shirt sleeve you find a wound in which you can see the end of a broken bone. The wound is still bleeding. What do you do? (List at least 4 appropriate actions.)

_____

_____

_____

_____

Scenario 2: Stairway Fall

A co-worker loses his footing coming down the last 2 steps of a stairway and falls forward, breaking his fall with an outstretched arm. He calls for help and you find him sitting on the bottom step, using his left hand to hold his right forearm close to his body. He tells you his right shoulder really hurts and he can't move it. He is wearing a thick shirt and you cannot see whether there is any swelling or deformity, but there is apparently no bleeding. You ask someone to call 9-1-1.

What else should you do before help arrives? Circle Y or N for each of the following actions that you should do or not do.

Y N Have him straighten his arm so you can remove his shirt.

Y N Immediately splint the arm with a board.

Y N Immobilize and support the arm and shoulder in the position found.

Y N Ask the victim if he is able to walk to your car to go to the hospital.

Y N Put an ice bag or cold pack on the painful injured area.

Y N Watch for signs and symptoms of shock.

Y N Elevate the arm over his head.

Sprains

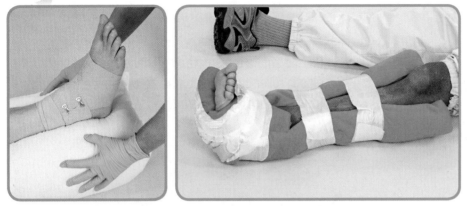

How long should ice be kept on a sprain or other injury?

Keep the ice on for _____ minutes (unless it is uncomfortable), then remove it for _____ minutes and then reapply it for _____ minutes (unless uncomfortable).

Care of Muscle Injuries

Consult your *First Aid Quick Guide* for the first aid steps for these muscle injuries:

- Muscle strain

- Muscle cramps

Always remember the acronym RICE for these and other injuries of bones, joints and muscles.

When to Splint?

- Splint an injury of the hand or foot if the victim is to be transported to the hospital in a personal vehicle.

- Splint any injury if help will be delayed and there is a risk of the injured area moving.

Check your *First Aid Quick Guide* under "Broken Bones and Dislocations" for how to splint common injuries.

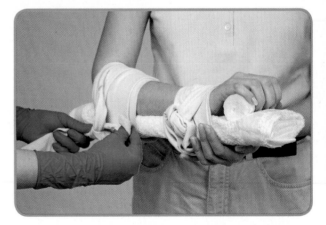

Learn the Skill

Applying a Roller Bandage

Pair up with a classmate to practice applying an elastic roller bandage around an extremity, such as for a sprained ankle or wrist.

Performance Checklist: Roller Bandage

Skill Step		Needs Practice	Proficient
1	Anchor the starting end of the bandage.		
2	Turn the bandage diagonally across the top of the foot and around the ankle, (or palm and wrist) and bring bandage around in a figure-eight.		
3	Continue with overlapping figure-eight turns.		
4	Fasten end of bandage with clips, tape or safety pins.		
	Complete Skill		

Things to Remember

FIRST AID FOR BONE, JOINT AND MUSCLE INJURIES

- You do not need to know the exact injury to give first aid.
- Call 9-1-1 for any large bone fracture or dislocation.
- Follow the RICE acronym for most injuries of bones, joints and muscles.

Lesson 13 • Sudden Illness

Objectives

✓ Describe the general signs and symptoms of sudden illness.

✓ List the general steps of first aid for sudden illness.

✓ Identify the first aid steps for:

- Asthma
- Fainting
- Stroke
- Seizures
- Diabetic emergencies
- Severe abdominal pain
- Respiratory distress

Video Review

General Signs and Symptoms of Sudden Illness

- Feeling ill, dizzy, confused or weak

- Skin color changes (flushed, pale or ashen)

- Sweating

- Nausea, vomiting

Any Sudden Illness

1. What can you do for a victim of any sudden illness if you do not recognize the specific problem?

_____

_____

_____

_____

Common Sudden Illnesses

Match the condition in the left column with a defining characteristic in the right column.

_____ 1. heart attack   a. convulsions

_____ 2. stroke   b. wheezing

_____ 3. seizure   c. fruity-smelling breath

_____ 4. diabetic emergency   d. persistent chest pain

_____ 5. asthma   e. 1-sided weakness

Remember: Heart attack is a common sudden illness – call 9-1-1 immediately when you see its signs and symptoms.

Asthma – A Common Breathing Problem

Signs and symptoms of asthma:

- Wheezing and difficulty breathing and speaking
- Dry, persistent cough
- Fear, anxiety
- Gray-blue or ashen skin
- Changing levels of responsiveness

What should you do when you see someone having an asthma attack?
Circle Y or N for each of the following actions that you should do or not do.

Y   N   Call 9-1-1 if the victim is not known to have asthma.

Y   N   Help the victim use his or her prescribed medication as directed.

Y   N   Have the victim breathe into a paper bag for a few minutes.

Y   N   Give the victim an aspirin as quickly as possible.

Y   N   Help the victim rest and sit in a position for easiest breathing.

Y   N   Have the victim lie on his or her back with feet raised.

 **Stroke**

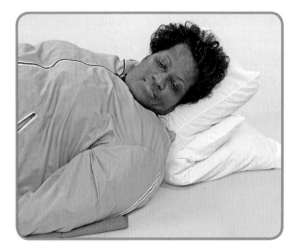

1. Which of the following are signs and symptoms that someone may be having a stroke? (Check all that apply.)

   ❑ High fever

   ❑ Numbness of face or arm on 1 side

   ❑ Bleeding from the nose and ears

   ❑ Drooling

   ❑ Sudden hunger

   ❑ Slurred speech

   ❑ Deformity in the extremities

2. The single most important thing to do for a stroke victim is to _____.

3. How should you position a responsive stroke victim while waiting for help to arrive? (Circle the best answer.)

   a. Have victim keep walking.

   b. Put victim in shock position with feet slightly raised.

   c. Have victim lie on back with head and shoulders slightly raised.

   d. Have victim sit and put head between knees.

Scenario 1: An Office Worker's Seizure

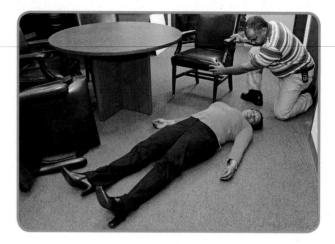

As you are walking past the office of Sheila, a co-worker, you hear an odd thump and look in to see that Sheila has fallen to the floor and is having a seizure. You remember that Sheila once told you she has been treated for epilepsy. You rush into the office to help.

Check your *First Aid Quick Guide* 📓.

1. What should you do first?

_____

2. Then what else can you do?

_____

_____

3. Should you call 9-1-1 in this case?

_____

Note: Always call 9-1-1 for a seizure victim if the person is not known to have epilepsy.

Diabetic Emergencies

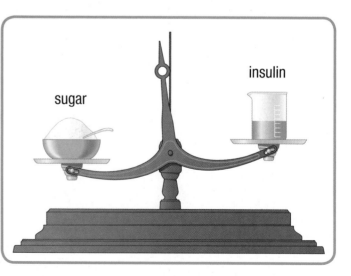

Low Blood Sugar	High Blood Sugar
• Sudden dizziness	• Frequent urination
• Shakiness	• Drowsiness
• Mood change	• Dry mouth
• Headache	• Thirst
• Confusion	• Shortness of breath
• Pale skin	• Deep, rapid breathing
• Sweating	• Nausea/vomiting
• Hunger	• Fruity-smelling breath

A diabetic emergency may occur if the body's balance of insulin and blood sugar is disrupted.

First Aid for Diabetic Emergencies

1. Give _____ to a victim experiencing low blood sugar.*

2. Call _____ if the victim becomes unresponsive or continues to have significant signs and symptoms.

Remember to check . . . .

✓ Ask the person if he or she is diabetic.

✓ Look for a medical alert ID.

✓ Look for a sugar substance to give the victim.

*If you don't know whether a diabetic person is experiencing low or high blood sugar, still give sugar. It will not further harm a victim experiencing high blood sugar, but it may save the life of a diabetic experiencing low blood sugar.

Fainting

Check your *First Aid Quick Guide* 📖 – When should you call 9-1-1 for fainting?

_____

_____

_____

_____

_____

Abdominal Pain

Check your *First Aid Quick Guide* — When should you seek medical attention for an adult with abdominal pain?

_____

_____

_____

_____

_____

_____

<table>
<tr><td>Things to Remember</td><td>

FIRST AID FOR ANY SUDDEN ILLNESS

- Call 9-1-1 for any unexplained sudden illness.
- Help the victim rest.
- Prevent the victim from becoming chilled or overheated.
- Reassure the victim.
- Do not give the victim anything to eat or drink.
- Watch for changes and be prepared to give basic life support.
</td></tr>
</table>

Lesson 14 • Allergic Reactions

Objectives

✓ List the causes of allergic reaction shock.

✓ Identify the first aid for allergic reaction shock.

✓ Demonstrate how to use an epinephrine auto-injector for a victim with a severe allergic reaction.

✓ Determine the first aid for a victim of poison ivy, oak or sumac.

Video Review

1. A person with serious allergies may be carrying _____.

2. True or false: Once a person with a serious allergic reaction has administered the EpiPen, you no longer need to call 9-1-1.

Learn the Skill

Anaphylactic Shock

Pair up with a classmate to practice administering emergency epinephrine to a victim with a severe allergic reaction. *Practice this skill only using an EpiPen training simulator – never with an actual EpiPen containing a needle and medication.*

Performance Checklist: Medication for Anaphylactic Shock

	Skill Step	Needs Practice	Proficient
1	Help a responsive victim use his or her emergency epinephrine kit such as an EpiPen auto-injector. If the victim cannot use the prescribed auto-injector, you may administer it yourself if permitted by state law.		
2	Take the EpiPen out of its case and remove the cap.		
3	To administer the medication, the victim jabs the pen tip into the outer thigh and holds it there for 10 seconds while the medication is injected. *The medication should provide relief for 15-20 minutes.*		
4	Monitor the victim's breathing and be ready to give basic life support if needed.		
5	Help a responsive victim sit up in a position of easiest breathing. Put an unresponsive victim who is breathing (if no suspected spinal injury) in the Recovery Position.		
	Complete Skill		

Allergic Reactions to Poison Ivy, Oak and Sumac

Poison ivy

Poison oak

Do you know what to do if you come in contact with one of these plants? (If not, check your *First Aid Quick Guide* 📖.)

Poison sumac

_____

_____

_____

Things to Remember

FIRST AID FOR ANAPHYLACTIC SHOCK

Possible causes of allergic reactions include:
- Certain drugs such as penicillin
- Certain foods such as peanuts and shellfish
- Certain substances such as latex
- Insect stings and bites

Signs and symptoms
- Difficulty breathing, wheezing, tightness in throat or chest
- Swelling of the face and neck, puffy eyes
- Anxiety or agitation
- Nausea, vomiting
- Changing levels of responsiveness

First Aid
1. Call 9-1-1.
2. Help a responsive victim use his or her emergency epinephrine kit such as an EpiPen auto-injector. If the victim cannot use the prescribed auto-injector, you may administer it yourself if permitted by state law:
   - Take the EpiPen out of its case and remove the cap.
   - To administer the medication, the victim jabs the pen tip into the outer thigh and holds it there for 10 seconds while the medication is injected.
   - The medication should provide relief for 15-20 minutes.
3. Monitor the victim's breathing and be ready to give basic life support if needed.
4. Help a responsive victim sit up in a position of easiest breathing. Put an unresponsive victim who is breathing in the recovery position

Lesson 15 • Poisoning

Objectives

✓ Identify when to call the Poison Control Center or 9-1-1 in cases of poisoning.

✓ Identify first aid steps for victims of swallowed poison.

✓ Identify first aid steps for victims of inhaled poison.

✓ In industrial settings, know the location and effects of chemicals, the Material Safety Data Sheets (MSDSs) and other chemical emergency information and the location of antidote supplies.

✓ Identify the steps of first aid for a victim of:

- A snake bite
- A bee or wasp sting
- A spider bite
- A scorpion sting
- A tick bite

Video Review

Circle T for true or F for false for each of the following statements.

1. T F   Call the Poison Control Center only if you know the exact ingredients in the poison that might have been involved.

2. T F   Never induce vomiting for a poisoning victim.

3. T F   Carbon monoxide poisoning from a faulty home furnace may cause headache, nausea and changing levels of responsiveness.

4. T F   Accidentally taking too much of a prescribed or over-the-counter medication may cause a poisoning emergency.

Scenario 1: Uncle Joe

You arrive home late in the afternoon and find Uncle Joe, who is elderly and has health problems, unresponsive on the kitchen floor. You quickly check and determine that he is breathing. You carefully position him in the recovery position and as you cross the room to the telephone, you notice on the table several pill bottles. One is open and a number of capsules have spilled out on the table. You believe that Uncle Joe might be experiencing an overdose poisoning.

1. On the wall beside the telephone is the number for the Poison Control Center: 800-222-1222. Should you call the Poison Control Center or 9-1-1? Why?

2. Why did you put him in the recovery position?

3. What do you do now while waiting for help to arrive?

Bites and Stings

Rattlesnake

Copperhead

Water moccasin

Coral snake

Indian or spectacled cobra (Naja naja)

Yellow eyelash pit viper

Black widow

Brown recluse

- The venomous snakes in the United States are rattlesnakes, copperheads, water moccasins (cottonmouths) and coral snakes. Outside the United States, common venomous snakes include the Indian or spectacled cobra (South Asia) and the yellow eyelash pit viper (South America).

- The venomous spiders in the United States are black widow and brown recluse spiders.

- Some scorpions are venomous.

- Call 9-1-1 for any poisonous bite or sting. See your *First Aid Quick Guide* for additional first aid until help arrives.

- Remember that bee and wasp stings may cause an allergic reaction. Call 9-1-1 if symptoms occur. See your *First Aid Quick Guide* for the signs and symptoms and first aid for allergic reactions.

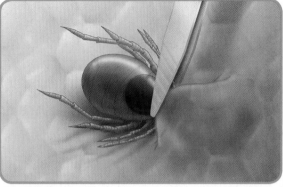

Tick bites can cause Lyme disease. Remove a tick by pulling gently.

Things to Remember

FIRST AID FOR SWALLOWED POISONS

1. Determine what was swallowed, when and how much.
2. For a responsive victim, call the national Poison Control Center **(800-222-1222)** immediately and follow its instructions.
3. For a victim with signs of a life-threatening condition and for an unresponsive victim, call 9-1-1 and provide basic life support as needed.
4. Put a breathing, unresponsive victim in the recovery position and be prepared for vomiting. Monitor the victim's breathing and be ready to give basic life support if needed.
5. Do not give the victim any substance to eat or drink unless instructed by the Poison Control Center.
6. If a responsive victim's mouth or lips are burned by a corrosive chemical, rinse the mouth with cold water (without allowing the victim to swallow).

First Aid for Inhaled Poisons
1. Immediately move the victim to fresh air.
2. Call 9-1-1 even if the victim starts to recover.
3. Monitor the victim and give basic life support as needed.
4. Put an unresponsive victim in the recovery position.
5. Loosen tight clothing around the neck or chest.

Lesson 16 • Cold and Heat Emergencies

Objectives

✓ List the signs of a cold emergency.

✓ Determine the first aid for frostbite.

✓ Describe the first aid for hypothermia.

✓ List the signs of a heat emergency.

✓ Determine the first aid for heat cramps.

✓ Determine the first aid for heat exhaustion.

✓ Identify the first aid for heatstroke.

Video Review

1. Which of the following are signs and symptoms of severe hypothermia?

   ❑ Victim feels feverish

   ❑ Victim seems drowsy, confused or irrational

   ❑ Lethargy, clumsy movements

   ❑ Skin is very red

   ❑ Pale, cool skin–even under clothing

   ❑ Frequent need to urinate

   ❑ Slow breathing

   ❑ Changing levels of responsiveness

2. For an unresponsive victim with severe hypothermia, check for
   _____ and call _____.

3. Warm a victim with hypothermia using _____ or _____

4. For a heatstroke victim, list 3 ways to cool the person's body as quickly as possible:

   _____

   _____

   _____

Cold and Heat Injuries

Hypothermia and heatstroke are life-threatening emergencies. Frostbite and heat exhaustion are usually less serious.

Prevent heat and cold injuries by dressing appropriately and avoiding prolonged exposure to temperature extremes. Stay well hydrated and rested.

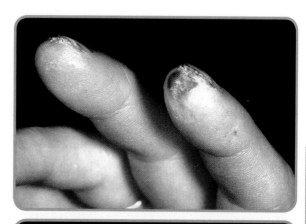

First Aid for Frostbite

1. Move the victim out of the cold and into a warm place.

2. Remove wet clothing and constricting items.

3. Protect between fingers and toes with dry gauze.

4. Seek medical attention as soon as possible.

5. Warm frostbitten area in lukewarm water (99 to 104 degrees F or 37 to 40 degrees C) for 20-30 minutes only if medical care will be delayed and there is no danger of it refreezing.

6. Protect and elevate the area.

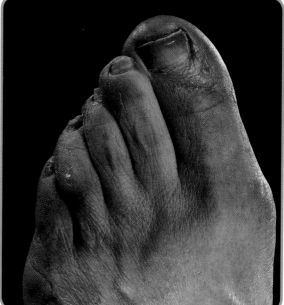

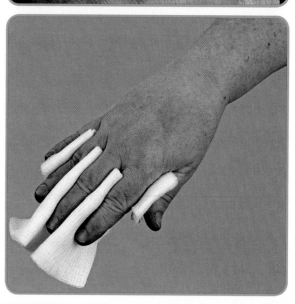

First Aid for Hypothermia

1. For an unresponsive victim, check for breathing and provide basic life support as needed. Call 9-1-1 for all severe hypothermia victims.

2. Quickly get the victim out of the cold and remove any wet clothing.

3. Have the victim lie down and cover him or her with blankets or warm clothing. If outdoors, put a blanket or clothing under the victim as well. Do not let a responsive victim move around.

4. Except in mild cases, the victim needs immediate medical care.

5. Only if the victim is far from medical care, use active rewarming by putting the victim near a heat source and putting warm water in containers against the skin.

6. Do not rub or massage the victim's skin. Be very gentle when handling the victim.

7. Give warm (not hot) drinks to an alert victim who can easily swallow, but do not give alcohol or caffeine.

Heat Exhaustion

Heat exhaustion will develop into heatstroke if the victim is not cooled and given water.

Signs and Symptoms of Heat Exhaustion

- Heavy sweating, thirst, fatigue or heat cramps

- Later headache, dizziness, nausea or vomiting

- May develop into heatstroke

First Aid for Heat Exhaustion

1. Move the victim out of the heat to lie down in a cool place, and loosen or remove outer clothing.

2. Cool the victim with a cool water spray or wet cloths on the forehead and body.

3. Give the victim a sports drink or water.

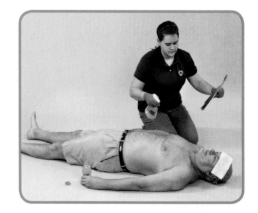

First Aid for Heatstroke

1. Call 9-1-1.

2. Move the victim to a cool place.

3. Remove outer clothing.

4. Immediately cool the victim with any means at hand, preferably by immersing the victim up to the neck in cold water (with the help of a second rescuer). Other methods include wrapping the victim in a wet sheet that you keep wet; sponging the victim with cold water; spraying the skin with water and fanning the area; or applying ice bags or cold packs beside the neck, armpits and groin).

5. Do not give any beverage containing caffeine or alcohol. If the victim is nauseous or vomiting or has diminished mental status, do not give any liquids.

6. Monitor the victim's breathing and be ready to give basic life support if needed.

 ## Scenario 1: The Company Picnic

Your company's annual picnic and softball game happens to fall on the hottest day of the year. By the seventh inning, your team's center fielder seems to be showing signs and symptoms of heatstroke.

1. Name 2 signs or symptoms that strongly suggest heatstroke.

   _____

   _____

2. What are the first steps you should take?

   _____

   _____

   _____

Things to Remember

FIRST AID FOR COLD AND HEAT EMERGENCIES

First Aid for Hypothermia
- Call 9-1-1 and give basic life support as needed.
- Move victim to warm place and remove wet clothes.
- Warm victim with blankets.
- Use active rewarming only if help will be delayed.
- Be gentle with victim.
- Give warm drink to alert victim but no alcohol or caffeine.

First Aid for Heatstroke
- Call 9-1-1 and give basic life support as needed.
- Move victim to cool place and remove outer clothing.
- Immediately cool victim with cold water.
- Do not give alcohol or caffeine.

Lesson 17 • Rescuing and Moving Victims

Objectives

✓ Describe what to do when a victim needs to be rescued from a dangerous situation.

✓ Describe what to do when multiple victims need first aid.

✓ Identify situations in which it is acceptable to move a victim.

✓ Describe how to move a victim when necessary.

Victim Rescue

- Never put yourself at risk to rescue a victim.
- When hazards are present, leave the rescue to the professionals. Call 9-1-1.
- Do not try to perform any rescue technique you have not been trained to do.

Multiple Victims

Quickly check all victims and give care first to the highest-priority victims who cannot wait for help.

Priorities for Multiple Victims

Priority	Victim's Condition	Severity	Examples
1st	Critical	Victims with life-threatening injuries who cannot wait for help	Airway or breathing problems Severe bleeding Shock Severe burn
2nd	Serious	Victims with injuries that need care very soon but may be able to wait for help	Burns Broken bones Other injuries not severely bleeding
3rd	Stable	Victims who can wait for some time	Minor injuries Victims who can walk
4th	Obviously dead or dying	Victims who cannot be saved	No signs of breathing and signs of severe bleeding (unless there are no 1st-priority victims)

Moving Victims Safely

- Moving a victim is liable to cause further injury.
- Move a victim only if the situation requires it.
- If you are not physically able to move the victim yourself, get help from others.
- Support the head and neck as much as possible.

2-rescuer assist

Shoulder drag

Piggyback carry

Cradle carry

Things to Remember

RESCUING AND MOVING VICTIMS

- Never risk your own safety in an attempt to rescue a victim from a dangerous situation. Call 9-1-1 and leave it to the professionals with the right training and equipment.
- With multiple victims, first treat those with life-threatening injuries who cannot wait for help but who can be saved.
- Consider moving an injured victim *only* if:
  - The scene becomes unsafe (risk of fire or explosion, poisonous fumes, structural collapse)
  - The victim needs to be moved into position for lifesaving care such as CPR
  - The victim is in the way of a more seriously injured victim

Answer Sheet: NSC First Aid, CPR and AED

Name _____ Date_____

1. a   b   c   d
2. a   b   c   d
3. a   b   c   d
4. a   b   c   d
5. a   b   c   d
6. a   b   c   d
7. a   b   c   d
8. a   b   c   d
9. a   b   c   d
10. a   b   c   d
11. a   b   c   d
12. a   b   c   d
13. a   b   c   d
14. a   b   c   d
15. a   b   c   d
16. a   b   c   d
17. a   b   c   d
18. a   b   c   d
19. a   b   c   d
20. a   b   c   d